PACEMAKER®

Economics

WORKBOOK

GLOBE FEARON

Pearson Learning Group

Pacemaker® Economics Third Edition

Reviewers
We thank the following educators, who provided valuable comments and suggestions during the development of this book:

Pacemaker Curriculum Advisor: Stephen C. Larsen, formerly of the University of Texas at Austin
Subject Area Consultant: Don R. Leet, Ph.D., California State University, Fresno, California

Project Staff
Executive Editor: Jane Petlinski
Project Manager: Suzanne Keezer
Project Editor: Renée Beach
Associate Production Editor: Amy Benefiel
Lead Designer: Joan Jacobus
Market Manager: Katie Erezuma
Manufacturing Supervisor: Mark Cirillo
Series Cover Design: Evelyn Bauer

About the Cover
Whether you realize it or not, you already know a lot about economics. The images on the cover represent items that are related to economics. Money, savings bonds, and stocks are all part of the economy. The price of goods and services that you use every day are affected by economics. In what other ways can economics affect your life?

ISBN: 0-130-23616-0

Printed in the United States of America

5 6 7 8 9 10   04 03

1-800-321-3106
www.pearsonlearning.com

Contents

A Note to the Student

The exercises in this workbook go along with your *Pacemaker Economics* textbook. Each exercise in this workbook is linked to a chapter in your textbook. This workbook gives you the opportunity to do three things—review, practice, and think critically.

The review exercises are questions and activities that test your knowledge of the information presented in the textbook. Set goals for yourself and try to meet them as you complete each activity. Being able to remember and apply information is an important skill, and leads to success on tests, in school, at work, and in life.

The skill practice exercises help you to apply economic and social studies skills. You will need these skills as you read and write about the information you have learned in your textbook. Some pages in the workbook have charts and graphs. These pages will give you extra practice in using your chart and graph skills.

Your critical thinking skills are challenged when you complete the critical thinking exercises. Critical thinking— or to put it another way, thinking critically—means putting information to use. For example, you may review and recall information about the high and low points of business cycles. Later you might use that information to explain what happened during the Great Depression of the 1930s. When you apply what you know to a different situation, you are thinking critically.

Your textbook is a wonderful source of knowledge. By using it along with this workbook, you will learn a great deal about economics. The real value of the information will come when you have mastered the skills and put them to use by thinking critically.

Name _____ Date _____

 1 ▸ Studying Vocabulary   **Exercise 1**

A. Fill in the chart below. Review Chapter 1 in your textbook if you
   need help.

Words to Know	Definitions	Examples
goods	1.	2.
3.	things provided by nature	4.
capital	5.	machines, tools
labor	6.	7.
8.	an activity performed for others for money	teaching, nursing
9.	whatever is given up when a choice is made	vacation you gave up to pay dentist
scarcity	10.	11.

B. Read and answer the questions.

1. In your opinion, what is the world's most important resource?

_____

_____

2. What goods or services would you find it difficult or even
   impossible to live without?

_____

_____

3. What goods or services would you tell people to give up in order to
   save money?

_____

_____

Name_____ Date_____

 1 ▶ Defining Economics   **Exercise 2**

A. Economics is the study of how people, businesses, and
governments choose to use their limited resources. Resources
include capital and natural resources. Give examples of each
resource listed below.

   1. Capital:

   _____

   _____

   2. Natural resources:

   _____

   _____

B. Economics is all about choices. Every day, people, businesses, and
governments make choices about how to earn money and how
to spend it. Give some examples by completing the sentences below.

   1. Some ways I might earn money include:

   _____

   2. Some ways I might spend money include:

   _____

   3. To earn more money, a business might:

   _____

   4. A business might spend money on things such as:

   _____

   5. One way the U.S. government raises money is by:

   _____

   6. The U.S. government spends money on things such as:

   _____

Name _____   Date _____

 1 ▶ **Learning About Economics**   **Exercise 3**

Read the following story. Then answer the questions.

Economics and You

"Economics? Why would I want to take economics?" asked Joe. He and his friends, Kayla and David, had met for lunch at a deli. They were talking about their classes. "I bet you can't even tell me what this economics stuff is," said Joe.

Kayla grinned. "Sure I can. Economics is the study of how people, businesses, and governments choose to use their limited resources."

"Okay," Joe laughed. "You get the gold star. But what has any of it got to do with me?"

"Everything," said David. "Let me ask you this. Why did you spend money on lunch? Why not spend it on that sports magazine you like so much?"

"Hey, I've got to eat. Sure, I want the magazine. But I need the food, and I've only got so much money."

"Well, Joe," Kayla jumped in. "That's economics. Economics is all about choices, like the way you chose between your needs and wants. Our economics teacher would say that you were solving the problem of scarcity."

"I get it," said Joe. "When you only have so much of something, you think about the best way to use it."

"Exactly," said David. "You see, all goods and services are produced with limited resources—and I don't just mean money. There are natural resources like water, air, oil, land, and so forth. Remember how we all tried to use less water during the dry years? We were conserving our resources."

"Capital is another resource," said Kayla. "That includes machines and tools that are used to produce goods and services. If I didn't have a car or bike, I couldn't deliver the newspaper."

"Don't forget labor," said David. "It's another resource."

"You mean workers?" asked Joe. David and Kayla nodded. "So that's what *human resources* means."

---

1. What economic problem did Joe face, and how did he solve it?

   _____

2. Besides money, what three kinds of resources did Kayla and David talk about? Give an example of each kind.

   _____

   _____

   _____

1 ▶ Starting a Business

Suppose you are an entrepreneur. Answer the questions below about your new business.

1. What kind of business are you going to start? Why did you choose this business?

   _____

   _____

   _____

2. What factors of production will you need? Complete the planning chart below.

Factors of Production	Examples That Have to Do With Your Business
a.	
b.	
c.	
d.	

3. Will you specialize? Why or why not?

   _____

   _____

4. List three ways you will use technology to make your business a success.

   _____

   _____

   _____

5. How will your business be good for consumers, your workers, and yourself?

   _____

   _____

   _____

2 ▶ Completing a Venn Diagram

Exercise 5

Skill Practice

You learned in Chapter 2 that there are three basic types of economic systems: traditional, market, and command. Use the Venn diagram below to compare and contrast any two of those systems. A Venn diagram is a type of chart made up of two overlapping circles. It is used to list similarities and differences between two items. Write the name of each system below the circles. In each separate section, write what is different about the economic system. In the shared section, write what the systems have in common.

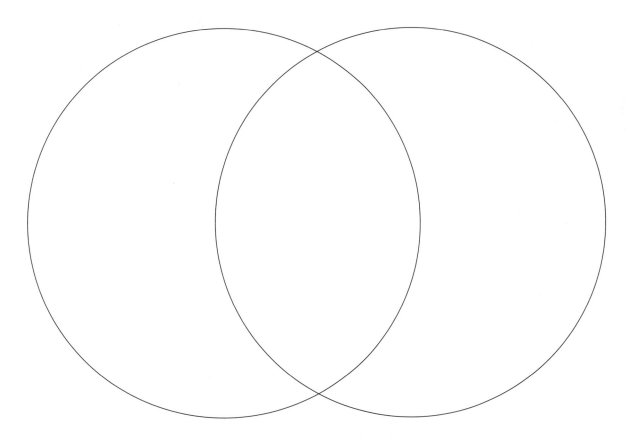

Economic System: _____   Economic System: _____

Name _____ Date _____

 Comparing Economic Systems

Read each situation below. Then answer the questions.

1. Estella is from a small village in Mexico. Suppose that she moved to Los Angeles, California. What do you think she would like best about shopping for goods in the city?

   _____

   _____

   _____

2. While on an airplane trip in his country, Keller decides that his ticket cost too much and that the food was not good. Keller lives in a command system. The government controls goods and services. Do you think that Keller will e-mail the airline complaining about his flight? Why or why not? How might things be different if the airline were part of a free-enterprise system?

   _____

   _____

   _____

3. How did you think your life would change if the United States switched from a market economy to a traditional system? How would you feel about those changes and why?

   _____

   _____

   _____

4. More Western businesses are finding their way into Eastern European and Central Asian markets. For example, you can now buy fast food and blue jeans in Baku. In your opinion, what is good about this trend? What is not good about this trend?

   _____

   _____

   _____

2 ▶ Writing a Report

A. You are a reporter for a business magazine. Your job is to write about one economic system and the group of people who use that system. To prepare your report, answer the questions below.

1. Which economic system will you write about?

_____

2. Where is this system used?

_____

_____

_____

3. What do you like about this system?

_____

_____

_____

_____

4. What do you dislike about this system?

_____

_____

_____

_____

B. On a separate sheet of paper, use the information above to write a news report. Be sure to:

- Add an interesting headline telling what the report is all about.
- Draw a map to show where the economic system exists.
- Add a drawing or magazine photo. It could show goods, services, people, or places that have to do with that system.

Name_____ Date_____

2 ▶ **Explaining Economic Differences**

Exercise 8

Read these letters. Then answer the questions.

> *Dear Gail,*
>   *I am happy to have an American pen pal. I am writing a paper for school. It's about different kinds of economic systems. I guess that the United States is a pure market economy. Am I right?*
>
> *Sincerely,*
> *Rakiya*

> Dear Rakiya,
>   You're almost right! The United States is not a pure market economy. The government does have some say in how goods and services are produced. It's a good thing, too. You see, I work part time at a fast-food restaurant. If we lived in a pure market economy, the owners could pay me as little as they wanted. However, the government sets minimum wages for workers. That's just one example of how laws affect business here.
>   Like all economies, ours is a mix of market, command, and traditional. But the United States is mainly a market economy. Everyone has the right to own property. Most businesses are owned by individuals. My dad runs an Internet-based business from home. That way, he can take care of my baby brother. My mom is a doctor. She thinks I'd be a good doctor, too. No thanks! I plan to start my own restaurant. I'll be free to compete against other restaurants. I can keep any profits that I earn. Best of all, I can buy what I like.
>   Good luck with your paper!
>
> Best wishes,
> *Gail*

1. Do you think that Gail and her family would enjoy living in a traditional economy? Why or why not?

_____

_____

2. Gail gives one example of how government can affect the production of goods and services. What is another example?

_____

_____

Name _____   Date _____

Use the graph to answer the questions below.

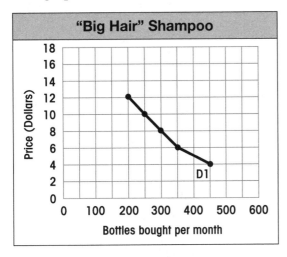

"Big Hair" Shampoo

Price (Dollars)

18
16
14
12
10
8
6
4
2
0

0   100   200   300   400   500   600

Bottles bought per month

D1

1. At $12 each, how many bottles of "Big Hair" shampoo will consumers buy per month?

   _____

2. How many bottles per month will consumers buy at $6 each?

   _____

3. If the demand curve shifts to the left, has demand increased or decreased? How might a change in consumer tastes cause this to happen?

   _____

4. If the demand curve shifts to the right, has demand increased or decreased? How might a change in incomes cause this to happen?

   _____

5. What are some complementary goods for shampoo?

   _____

6. If the demand curve for "Big Hair" shampoo shifts to the left, is the price of complementary goods more likely to rise or fall? Explain.

   _____

3 ▶ **Studying Vocabulary**   **Exercise 10**

A. Choose the correct term from the box to match the definitions.

complementary goods	law of demand	income
demand	substitute goods	

1. _____ the economic law that states that consumers will buy more of a good or service as the price goes down

2. _____ the amount of money people make in a certain time period

3. _____ the amount of a good or service that consumers are willing and able to buy at different prices

4. _____ goods that can be used in place of one another

5. _____ goods that are often used together

B. Write about any two of the terms listed above. Give examples to show how those terms can change consumer demand.

_____

_____

_____

_____

_____

_____

_____

_____

_____

3 ▶ **Completing a Survey**   **Exercise 11**

A. Read and answer the questions.

Meat Product Survey

1. How many meat products does your family buy at the grocery store now compared to a few years ago?

    Fewer   About the same   More

2. If you answered "fewer" or "more," which of the following had something to do with the change?

    A change in the cost of meat products

    A change in your income

    A change in your attitude about eating meat

3. If the price of meat doubled, what do you think buyers would do?

    Buy as much meat as before

    Buy less meat

    Stop buying meat

4. If you answered "stop buying meat," what do you think people might buy as a substitute?

_____

_____

B. If consumers continue to buy fewer meat products, how do you think it will affect the economy?

_____

_____

_____

_____

_____

_____

3 ▷ **Reading Ads**   **Exercise 12**

Critical Thinking

Reading newspaper ads and articles can tell you a lot about the state of the economy. Read the following. Then answer the questions.

THE NEWS July 5, 2001

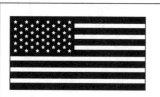

AMERICAN FLAGS
Were $49.95
Now only $19.95

ON SALE AT SUE'S SUPERMARKET

Real cocoa.............$4.89
Chocolate drink........$1.49
Spaghetti...............$ .99
Spaghetti sauce.........$2.25
Bread...................$1.63
Cookies................$ .88
Frozen yogurt..........$3.99
Ice cream..............$2.50

FASHION...

RED HATS ARE RED HOT
Hollywood—It all began when Ima Star showed up at the Oscars in a red hat. Fans around the world saw Ima Star on TV. They loved that hat. At the time, it sold for $12. Now buyers are paying up to $100 to get one just like it. But the fad can't last. After all, consumers say they like the hat because it is different. But soon, everybody will have one. And then? Why, it will all be...old hat!

MORE STORIES INSIDE
Consumers Stay Home.......................C1
Average Income Drops.....................E1
Cost of Living Soars.........................E2

1. Why do you think the price of flags has suddenly dropped so low?

_____

2. What might flag sellers do in November as Veterans' Day draws near? Why?

_____

3. What complementary goods are on sale at Sue's Supermarket? If you were choosing between pairs of substitute goods, which would you buy?

_____

_____

4. Which probably had more of an effect on the demand for red hats, incomes or consumer tastes? How can you tell?

_____

4 ▶ Using a Graph

The graph below shows a shift in the supply curve for leather hiking boots. Use the graph to answer the questions. Review Chapter 4 in your textbook if you need help.

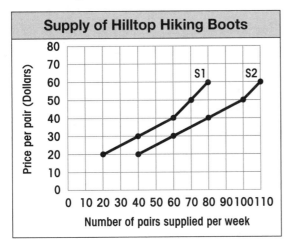

Supply of Hilltop Hiking Boots

1. Has the supply curve shifted to the right or to the left?

   _____

2. Has supply increased or decreased?

   _____

3. Circle the choice below that gives a possible explanation for this change. Give a reason for your choice.

   a. The cost of leather went up.

   b. Fashion designers said platform shoes were back in style.

   c. The company switched from hand stitching to machine stitching.

   _____

4. Suppose that the company moved its factory from the United States to a country where the costs of hiring workers were much lower. Based on the change in labor costs, do you think the company would start producing more or fewer hiking boots? Explain your answer. Use a separate sheet of paper if you need more space.

   _____

   _____

   _____

   _____

Defining the Law of Supply

A. Read the following article. Then answer the questions.

What Affects the Law of Supply?

The law of supply states that when the price of a good or service rises, producers will usually be willing and able to supply more of that good or service. However, supply can be affected by the cost of production, technology, and opportunity costs.

For example, suppose the price of fresh oranges suddenly goes up. This means the production costs for orange juice will go up. The producers may decide to make fewer cartons of orange juice. This will cause a decrease in the supply of orange juice.

Better technology can help increase supply. Suppose a new machine is invented. The machine helps turn the oranges into juice. It saves the producers a lot of time and labor costs. The producers decide to supply more cartons of orange juice.

Opportunity costs can affect supply, too. Suppose apple juice becomes much more popular than orange juice. The producers of orange juice may discover that they can make more of a profit by making apple juice.

---

1. Suppose you invent a machine that quickly turns oranges into juice. Describe how the machine increases production.

   _____

   _____

   _____

   _____

   _____

2. How will the machine affect production costs?

   _____

   _____

   _____

   _____

B. On a separate sheet of paper, draw what your new juice machine looks like. Label the parts of the machine.

Name _____   Date _____

Answer the following questions from a seller's point of view.

   1. Suppose you could make and sell a product. What kind of product would it be?

   _____

   _____

   _____

   2. List two production costs that might go into the making of your product.

   _____

   _____

   3. One of your production costs goes up. How might that affect the supply of
   your product?

   _____

   _____

   _____

   4. How might technology help you increase your supply?

   _____

   _____

   _____

   5. How might competition affect your costs?

   _____

   _____

   _____

   _____

   _____

4 ▶ Selling a Service

Answer the following questions from a seller's point of view.

1. Suppose you could sell a service. What kind of service would it be?

_____

_____

2. How much money would you charge for each hour of that service?
Give two reasons for your answer.

_____

_____

_____

3. Suppose demand for that service were high. How might that affect
your labor supply?

_____

_____

4. Suppose demand for that service were low. List three changes you
would make to increase demand.

_____

_____

_____

_____

_____

_____

_____

Name_____   Date_____

Use the graph to answer the questions below.

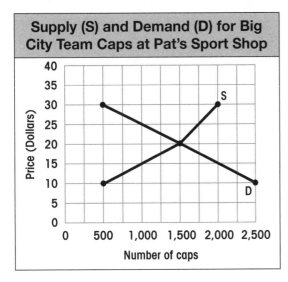

Supply (S) and Demand (D) for Big City Team Caps at Pat's Sport Shop

1. What is the equilibrium price of Big City team caps at Pat's Sport Shop?

    _____

2. Suppose the Big City team goes on a winning streak. What might happen to the equilibrium price of caps? Why?

    _____

    _____

3. What do you think might cause a surplus? Why?

    _____

    _____

4. If there is a surplus, what might Pat do to reduce inventory? What would happen to the equilibrium price as a result?

    _____

    _____

    _____

Name _____ Date _____

**Suppose you are the owner of a business that sells office machines and supplies.
Answer the questions.**

1. What a week! Ever since *Computer Lovers Magazine* gave the Hot Shot computer
   four stars, everybody seems to want one. You have three Hot Shot computers
   left. However, 15 people want to buy them. What will result from this? What
   will you do about it?

   _____

   _____

   _____

2. The Hot Shot computers cost $1,099 each. Because they are so popular, no one
   seems to care that you have 10 Niftee computers. Well, they do ask about
   them. However, when you tell them that the Niftees are just as good but a
   slightly higher price, they say, "Never mind. I'll just try to find a Hot Shot at
   some other store." What can you do to keep all those buyers from walking out
   the door? What will happen to the demand for Niftees as a result?

   _____

   _____

   _____

3. Look at that typewriter in the corner. It seems as if you have had it forever.
   Why do you think demand has gone down? One day, a student walks in and
   takes a look at it. The price is $200. The student says, "I'll give you $95."
   Describe the rest of the conversation. Tell how you and the student agree on a
   price. What is that price called?

   _____

   _____

   _____

4. Okay, you got rid of the typewriter. What will you do if someone offers you
   $900 for a Hot Shot computer? Why?

   _____

   _____

   _____

Name_____ Date_____

5 ▶ **Identifying Shortages and Surpluses**   **Exercise 19**

Every day, consumers are affected by shortages and surpluses. Read the following examples. Then answer the questions.

1. You see an ad for tickets to a concert by the most popular rock star in the United States. Which is more likely to happen, a surplus or a shortage? Why?

   _____

   _____

2. You see an ad for a furniture store. "Take a seat—please! Prices cut! Everything must go!" Do you think the store has a surplus or a shortage? Why?

   _____

   _____

3. Millions of people listen to a radio talk-show hosted by a doctor. Today, the doctor reports that eating a snack food called "Eat 'em Ups" may cause an upset stomach. Recently, the makers of "Eat 'em Ups" could hardly keep up with demand for their product. What do you think might happen now, and why?

   _____

   _____

4. You turn on the TV to watch the news and learn that a resort island has been hit by a hurricane. Several big hotels and thousands of houses have been destroyed. Only a few hundred construction workers live on the island. What are two ways that supply and demand will be affected?

   _____

   _____

5. In August, you see an ad for a preseason coat sale. One coat that you like costs $99. The ad tells you to buy now because the price will be $149 starting November 1. How do you explain the difference in equilibrium prices?

   _____

   _____

6 ▶ Role Playing Business Owners

Exercise 20

Critical Thinking

One of your classmates is a business owner. Interview the classmate using the following questions. Write the answers on the lines below.

1. What kind of business are you in?

   _____

2. Are you a partner or a sole proprietor?

   _____

3. What do you like best about that kind of ownership?

   _____

   _____

4. What are some of its disadvantages?

   _____

   _____

5. What made you decide to go into business?

   _____

   _____

6. What future plans do you have for your business?

   _____

   _____

7. What advice would you give to someone trying to choose between being a partner or a sole proprietor?

   _____

   _____

   _____

6 ▶ Buying a Franchise

Exercise 21

Review

Suppose you were buying and running your own business. However, you want to play it safe and buy a franchise. Choose a franchise you would like to buy, either real or imaginary. Then answer the questions.

1. What is the name of the company?

_____

2. How much is the start-up fee in exchange for using the company's name and products?

_____

3. Will the company help you find a location? Where do you think would be a good area?

_____

4. Does the company provide help with marketing? If so, what kind?

_____

_____

5. What rules and regulations must a franchise owner follow?

_____

_____

_____

6. You are asked to give a presentation of your ideas for new products or services to the franchise company. List three ideas below.

_____

_____

_____

_____

_____

_____

6 ▶ Identifying Types of Businesses

Exercise 22

Review

Read the following quotes. Decide whether the speaker works in a sole proprietorship, a partnership, or a corporation. Write your answer below each quote.

1. "Getting the business started was a complicated legal procedure."

   _____

2. "If this business succeeds, I'm the one responsible. That's the good news. The bad news? If it fails, I'm also the one responsible."

   _____

3. "Our profits can be taxed twice."

   _____

4. "I'm just one of many people who make the decisions."

   _____

5. "It's all fifty-fifty. We each pay half the bills, and we each get half the profits."

   _____

6. "People shop here because they trust me. I know most of my customers' names, too."

   _____

7. "I specialize in doing paperwork. You specialize in working with customers. But we share the decision making."

   _____

8. "I'm in charge. I can use the profits any way I like."

   _____

9. "We can't guarantee a profit to our shareholders. But when we do show a profit, we give some of it to them in the form of a dividend."

   _____

6 ▷ Owning a Business

Exercise 23

Critical Thinking

Read the story. Then answer the questions.

The Shoe Store

"I sure like your dad's shoe store," Cal said to Ashley.

"Thanks. But it's not just his store," Ashley said. "My Aunt Fran gets half the profits. Of course, she also gets half the work, half the bills, and half the headaches!"

"Still, they must be raking in the cash. Look how crowded this place is!"

"That's only because Dad and Fran decided to have a big sale. Last week, the store was almost empty," said Ashley.

"But you yourself said that revenues are up this year."

"That's true. But Fran and Dad have to use those revenues to pay for costs. They have to pay factories for the shoes and the staff for their work. That still leaves rent, which costs a lot at this mall. And taxes. And advertising. And so on. Subtract the total costs from the total revenues and—"

"And whatever is left is the profit?" asked Cal.

"That's right," said Ashley. "Dad and Fran share in the profits equally."

"Ashley, what happens if the total costs are more than the total revenues?"

"My dad and Fran get very nervous. That's just what happened last week when the store was so quiet. My dad and Fran still had to pay four employees who had no work to do!"

"I'm beginning to wonder why anyone would want their own business!" said Cal.

Just then, Ashley saw a familiar face. It was Mr. Costello, her P.E. teacher.

"That father of yours is one great guy," said Mr. Costello to Ashley. "He makes a big fuss over our twins whenever my family and I come in. Not like that Flying Feet Company where nobody knows us. You tell him and Fran I'll be bringing the entire track team in this Saturday."

Then Mr. Costello left. Ashley smiled. "Does that answer your question?"

---

1. Which of the three types of business is the shoe store?

_____

2. Ashley says that her dad and her aunt get very nervous when the total revenues are less than the total costs. What does she mean by that?

_____

3. How might they reduce their costs if business continued to be slow?

_____

4. Do you think the sale was a good idea or a bad idea, since it meant selling the shoes at lower prices? Explain your answer on a separate sheet of paper.

6 ▶ **Writing an Article**   **Exercise 24**

Congratulations! *Big Wigs* magazine wants you to write about your
life as an entrepreneur. Did you go from rags to riches, or from riches
to rags? Choose from the suggestions in the box to help you write
your article.

> • What kind of goods or services you sold
> • What it was like to start out as a sole proprietor
> • How things changed when you decided to bring in a partner
> • What happened when you wanted to form a corporation
> • Why your business showed a loss
> • How you made a profit
> • Why one business failed or succeeded
> • Why you chose the type of business you did

_____

_____

_____

_____

_____

_____

_____

_____

_____

_____

_____

_____

_____

Name _____   Date _____

 7 **Reading the Stock Listings**   **Exercise 25**

Find a sample stock market listing from your local newspaper or on the Internet. Choose any group of three listings. See what you can learn from the listing. Review Chapter 7 in your textbook, pages 94 and 95, if you need help. Use the information in the newspaper or online to fill in the chart below. Then attach your stock listing to this page.

Stock Market Listings						
Stock	**Year High**	**Year Low**	**Div**	**Sales (Hds)**	**Last**	**Net Chg**
1. ___	___	___	___	___	___	___
2. ___	___	___	___	___	___	___
3. ___	___	___	___	___	___	___

1. Which stock had the highest price in the last year? What was the price per share?

   _____

2. Which stock paid the lowest dividend? How much was the dividend per share?

   _____

3. Which stocks, if any, are preferred stocks? How can a reader tell?

   _____

4. Which stock sold the most shares on the day of this listing?

   _____

5. Which stock had the biggest net change?

   _____

6. If you could, would you invest in any of the stocks listed above? If yes, which one and why? If not, why not?

   _____

7. Look at the first listing on your chart. Suppose you bought 100 shares of that stock when it was at its lowest price in the last year. If you sold it at its highest price, how much would your capital gain be?

   _____

7 ▸ Defining Securities

Exercise 26

Review

Choose from the terms in the box. Write the correct word after each definition.

invest	preferred stock	common stock	capital gain	capital loss
stockbroker	stock market	bond	creditor	securities

1. Stock that offers the stockholder fixed dividends but does not give the stockholder voting rights _____

2. An IOU (the person who buys it is lending money to the government or corporation that sells it) _____

3. The money lost when you sell something for less than you paid for it

   _____

4. Stocks or bonds _____

5. A person or business who is owed money _____

6. A place where stocks and bonds are traded _____

7. To use money to earn interest or income in the hopes of making a profit

   _____

8. The money earned when you sell something for more than you paid for it

   _____

9. Stock that gives the stockholder voting rights but may or may not offer dividends

   _____

10. A person who is licensed to buy and sell stocks and bonds for other people

    _____

Name _____   Date _____

 7 ⟩ **Learning About the Stock Market**   **Exercise 27**

Answer the questions below. Share your own views.

1. Would you want the job of a stockbroker? Why or why not?

   _____

   _____

2. If you had $1,000 to invest, what would you do with it? Give
   reasons for your answer.

   _____

   _____

3. If you were thinking of buying stocks or bonds, what steps would
   you take to reduce your risks?

   _____

   _____

4. Would you rather own shares of preferred stock or common stock?
   Why?

   _____

   _____

5. Suppose two companies offer you the same job. Company A pays a
   little less than usual but gives shares of stock to its employees.
   Company B pays a little more than usual but does not give shares
   of stock to its employees. Which would you choose, and why?

   _____

6. What do you think is the most important thing people need to
   remember when it comes to investment? Why?

   _____

   _____

   _____

   _____

7 **Investing with Stockbrokers**   **Exercise 28**

Review

You are a stockbroker. Someone comes to you looking for information
about investing. What information and advice will you give them?
Answer the questions below.

1. This is all new to me. What is a stockbroker?

_____

_____

2. How can I make money buying and selling stock?

_____

_____

3. Can I be sure of making lots of money on the stock market? Why or why not?

_____

_____

4. I have heard of preferred stock and common stock. What is the difference?

_____

_____

5. Are stocks and bonds pretty much the same thing? How are they different?

_____

_____

6. I want to know what the stock market is doing every day. What are two ways
that I can do this?

_____

_____

_____

_____

Name _____ Date _____

8 ▶ Identifying Types of Businesses

Exercise 29

Review

You learned in Chapter 8 that most, but not all, businesses face competition from other businesses. Some facts about competition are listed in the box. Sort the facts. Then list them below the type of business in which they best belong.

---

a. It is easy to find information about prices, quality, and the availability of the good or service.

b. This kind of business has no competition.

c. There are many buyers and sellers.

d. These producers sell the same product.

e. It is difficult for others to sell the same good or service.

f. Most businesses are between perfect competition and monopoly.

g. It is easy for others to start the same business.

h. This includes some utility companies.

i. Shoe repair shops are an example of this.

---

1. Monopoly

_____

_____

_____

2. Perfect Competition

_____

_____

_____

3. Limited Competition

_____

_____

8 ▷ **Beating the Competition**   **Exercise 30**

Read the story. Then answer the questions.

How Becky Beat the Competition

When Becky's Book Barn opened in October, it was not the only bookstore in town. There were many others. The books and prices were pretty much the same in each store. However, Becky was sure that she could compete with the other sellers.

At first, Becky tried to compete by lowering her prices. This did not work. The owners of the other stores just did the same. Customers were happy, but bookstore owners were not. Their profits went down.

Becky thought about what she needed to do. She asked herself this question: When several stores sell similar products at similar prices, what do buyers do? Why, they go to the store that offers the best service! So Becky came up with a plan to offer the best service in town. She turned part of her bookstore into a reading room. She even put in soft chairs, paintings, and a fireplace. She offered free coffee, too.

Soon Becky was making more sales than the other stores. Her prices were the same as theirs. However, people said that a visit to Becky's Book Barn was more fun. Many buyers came from out of town just to see the reading room.

---

1. In this story, what does *competition* mean?

_____

_____

2. What happened when Becky lowered her prices?

_____

_____

3. Why did Becky draw more buyers than the other stores?

_____

_____

4. What do you think the other bookstore owners may do to increase their business?

_____

_____

8 ▶ Competing in Business

Exercise 31

Critical Thinking

Read and answer the questions.

1. Think about your favorite restaurant or store. Why do you like it better than its competitors? List four reasons.

_____

_____

_____

_____

2. If you were one of the competitors, what would you do to increase business?

_____

_____

_____

_____

3. Would everyone be better off if businesses agreed not to compete with each other? Why or why not?

_____

_____

_____

_____

_____

8 ▸ Writing a Consumer Report

Magazines and newspapers often carry consumer reports. These are comparisons of similar goods or services. For example, a consumer report about different brands of vegetable soup might include comparisons of price, amount of vegetables, taste, and cooking time. A survey of photo developers might look at cost per roll, speed of service, and quality of prints. Write your own consumer report by completing the information below.

1. Type of good or service you are investigating:

_____

2. Four things you look for in that good or service:

_____

_____

_____

_____

3. Other brands (or companies) you have used:

_____

_____

_____

_____

4. Which brand or company do you prefer?

_____

5. What factors make it your favorite?

_____

_____

_____

Date _____

9 ▶ Working for Wages

Read and answer the questions.

1. Who makes up the labor force? Give four examples.

_____

_____

_____

_____

2. Who is not part of the labor force? Give four examples.

_____

_____

_____

_____

3. What determines wages?

_____

_____

4. When the demand for a good or service is high, what happens to demand for labor in that industry?

_____

_____

5. Who do you think earns the most money, a ticket taker at a movie theater, a heart surgeon, or the manager of a computer store? Who do you think earns the least? Give two reasons for your answers.

_____

_____

_____

_____

9 ▸ Completing a Résumé

Exercise 34

Skill Practice

Several people apply for the same high-paying job. The job calls for
excellent communication skills and business know-how. Help J. Smith
get the job by adding important details to the résumé below.

J. Smith
1222 Times Way
Boulder, CO 94444
phone: (555) 555-1212 • e-mail: jsmith@gfecon.com

Education:

_____

_____

Work Experience:

_____

_____

Special Skills:

_____

_____

Community Activities:

_____

_____

References:

_____

_____

---

9 ▶ Using Automation

Exercise 35

Critical Thinking

A. You learned in Chapter 9 that automation can help workers or replace them. Use your ideas about automation to complete the following exercise.

1. You are working at the job you have always wanted. The hours are long. The work is hard, but the pay is good. What kind of job do you have?

   _____

   _____

2. One day, you get a memo from your boss. The memo says that the company is going to start using robots. On a separate sheet of paper, draw the robot. Add labels to show what the robot can do.

3. Are you now worried that a robot may replace you? Why or why not? List three reasons for your answer.

   _____

   _____

   _____

B. Banks use automatic teller machines. Fax machines and e-mail programs do the work of messengers. Many foods we eat are prepared by machines, not people. Automation affects us every day. Answer the following questions.

1. What is one business that you use often for goods and services?

   _____

2. How is automation used in that business?

   _____

   _____

3. Would you rather own a business that relied more on automation or on human workers? Give reasons for your answer.

   _____

   _____

   _____

9 ▶ Joining the Labor Force

Exercise 36

Review

Read the story. Then answer the questions.

Ellen Finds a Job

My name is Ellen. I am a computer specialist. I used to think I would be lucky to have any kind of job at all.

You see, for years I stayed home and raised my kids. Later, when I started looking for a job, no one wanted to hire me. They said that I had never worked before! But I think that being a mom is very hard work.

After several months, I applied for a job washing dishes at a restaurant. Fifty other people applied, too. But I was hired. The pay was $5.15 an hour. Not much. One of my co-workers told me that the boss could not pay me less than $5.15. If he did, he would be breaking the law.

I worked so hard, but I must say I hated my job. I kept getting these big ideas for helping the business. But the boss just said, "You take care of the dishes. I'll take care of the business."

I started going to college at night. It took a long time to finish, but it was worth it. Once I had a degree, I was able to work somewhere else. I made better money.

Every chance I got, I learned new skills. I had a real gift for learning languages. I was also good with computers.

One day, the owner of an international computer company offered me a top job. He was willing to pay me $150,000 a year. After all, I'm probably the only computer whiz in the United States who speaks four languages!

---

1. Ellen says that she worked hard during the years that she stayed at home. Was she a part of the labor force at that time? Why or why not?

_____

_____

2. There must be a great demand for dishwashers at restaurants, but the wages are not high. Why do you think this is the case?

_____

3. A co-worker told Ellen that the boss would be breaking the law if he paid her less than $5.15 an hour. What law is that?

_____

4. What determined the high salary for Ellen's job at the computer company?

_____

10 ▸ Learning About Labor Unions

Exercise 37

Review

Read and answer the questions.

1. How can both sides in a labor dispute work together if collective bargaining does not work?

   _____

   _____

2. What is an example of a successful boycott?

   _____

   _____

3. How is a strike different from a lockout?

   _____

   _____

   _____

4. What are some examples of fringe benefits?

   _____

   _____

   _____

5. How does a union shop differ from a closed shop?

   _____

   _____

   _____

10 ▶ Working Conditions

Think about the many changes one factory might go through in 150 years. Compare and contrast working conditions for employees in 1880 with what they might be like for employees in the year 2030.

Changes	Working Conditions	
	1880	**2030**
Name of the company		
Type of goods produced		
Kinds of technology used		
Average hours worked per week, per person		
Pay per hour		
Age of youngest employee		
How safe are conditions?		
What fringe benefits are there?		

10 ▸ Reading About Labor Organizations

Exercise 39

Critical Thinking

Read the following information about John L. Lewis, an important
labor leader in America. Then answer the questions.

A Labor Pioneer

John L. Lewis, son of immigrants from mining towns in Great Britain, left
school in the seventh grade and started working in the mines at age 15. He
became a legal representative for the United Mine Workers of America (UMWA) in
1905. From 1920 to 1960, he served as president of the UMWA. Lewis was also
founder and first president of the Congress of Industrial Organizations (CIO). He
became famous for organizing mass-production workers into industrial unions.
Members of his union were the first to receive welfare and retirement benefits.

---

1. Why do you think John L. Lewis was a good representative and
president of the UMWA?

_____

_____

2. Would you join a union? Why or why not?

_____

_____

3. What benefits do you think union members should receive?

_____

_____

_____

_____

_____

_____

_____

10 ▸ **Learning About César Chávez**   **Exercise 40**

Critical Thinking

Read the following information. Then answer the questions.

César Chávez

   César Chávez was best known as a union leader. Born in Arizona in 1927, Chávez began his working life as a migrant laborer. He traveled from job to job picking crops. Pickers worked long hours for low wages.

   In 1962, Chávez decided that things had to change. He organized grape pickers in California and formed the National Farm Workers Association (NFWA). The NFWA members used strikes, pickets, and marches to draw attention to their cause. Some people even fasted. They refused to eat until they got the changes that they wanted. The NFWA also asked consumers to boycott grapes. In the end, Chávez won contracts from several major growers of grapes.

   In 1966, the NFWA merged with the AFL-CIO to form the United Farm Workers of America.

   Chávez died in 1993.

---

1. What kind of organization is the United Farm Workers?

   _____

2. Do you think that farm workers had fringe benefits before 1962?
   Why or why not?

   _____

   _____

3. Do you think that those workers who fasted did the right thing?
   Why or why not?

   _____

   _____

   _____

4. The NFWA asked consumers to boycott grapes. What does that
   mean, and how would that affect events?

   _____

   _____

   _____

11 ▶ Protecting Consumers

Exercise 41

Critical Thinking

Read the paragraphs below. Write what you would do in each situation.

1. You bought a clock radio on sale at an appliance store. The clock does not keep accurate time. What should you do?

   _____

   _____

2. You just had the oil changed in your car. The next day, the oil is all over your driveway. What should you do?

   _____

   _____

3. You just washed a new sweater according to the instructions on the label. The sweater shrunk, and now it is too small to wear. What should you do?

   _____

   _____

4. There is a warning on the news from the Consumer Product Safety Commission about a toy that might be dangerous to small children. You have just bought the toy for your younger sister who is three years old. What should you do?

   _____

   _____

5. You read an ad in the newspaper for a mattress that is on sale. Once in the store, the manager tells you the mattress is no longer available. She tries to sell you a more expensive mattress. What should you do?

   _____

   _____

11 ▷ Giving Advice   **Exercise 42**

Read the following situations. Then answer the questions.

> Janet lives at home, but she wants to move into her own apartment. She spends $125 a month on gas and insurance for the car that her parents gave her. The rest she spends on clothes and entertainment. One day, Janet finds an apartment that rents for $600 a month. "No problem," she tells her best friend Suzan. "I make $1,000. Once I pay rent and car expenses, I'll have $275 left to spend on the fun stuff." "Janet," Suzan says with a grin, "are you planning on eating?"

1. What are two additional expenses that might come with renting an apartment?

_____

_____

> Raimund wants to have the carpets cleaned in his home. He is willing to spend $150 to $225 to get the work done. He gets out the Yellow Pages, looks up A-One Carpet Cleaners, and calls the number. He asks several questions and jots down notes. A-One says that it would charge $205 to clean all the carpets. Raimund then dials the number of Best Carpet Cleaners.

2. What else, besides price, would a shopper like Raimund ask about?

_____

> Jake tells Paul, "I really wish I could go to college, but it's just too expensive. How am I going to come up with the tuition by September?" "It's only March," says Paul. "You've got time. Besides, you live at home, and you work part time." "True," says Jake, "but I'm thinking of buying a brand-new car. I'm looking at car payments of $400 a month. It's a lot more than I want to spend just to get around town. On the other hand, it's a good-looking car! What do you think?" "I think you need to look at your priorities," says Paul.

3. What does Paul mean? What else can Jake do if he wants to go to college?

_____

_____

Name _____   Date _____

 11 **Planning a Budget**   **Exercise 43**

Complete the monthly budget based on the information that follows. Then answer the questions.

Your monthly income is $2,100 after taxes. You spend $650 in rent and $100 in utilities. Your phone bill averages $55 every month. You also spend $150 on groceries and another $30 a month on fast food. Fill in the remaining part of the budget so the total adds up to $2,100.

My Monthly Budget	
Monthly income (after taxes):	*$2,100*
Rent:	
Utilities:	
Telephone:	
Food:	
Clothing:	
Transportation:	
Total:	
Remaining income:	

What will you give up in your budget to save money? What are you not willing to give up?

_____

_____

11 ▶ Using a Budget

Use the budget you made in Exercise 43 to answer the questions.

1. Look over your budget. What are three other goods or services that you would need money for each month?

_____

_____

_____

2. Which good or service that you listed above is the most important to you? Why?

_____

_____

_____

_____

3. How much are you willing to spend each month on the good or service that you chose? Compare that amount to the amount shown for "remaining income" on your budget. Do you have enough money? If not, what will you do?

_____

_____

_____

4. Suppose you want to buy a new washer and dryer for $1,000. Look at the remaining income on your budget. How much money could you pay each month for these appliances? How long would it take you to pay off the $1,000?

_____

_____

12 ▶ Defining Bank Terms

Exercise 45

Review

Read the terms in the box. Then write the correct word next to its definition.

annually	certificate of deposit (CD)	financial institutions
withdraw	compound interest	credit
money market account	principal	time-deposit account
collateral		

Words to Know	**Definitions**
1. _____	Banks and other organizations that offer money-related services
2. _____	Property used as a guarantee of payment on a loan
3. _____	An account that requires money to be left in the account for a certain period of time
4. _____	Once a year
5. _____	The original amount of money borrowed on a loan
6. _____	A type of savings account with a fixed, higher interest rate than a regular savings account
7. _____	To take money out of an account
8. _____	Interest paid on the original deposit and on any earned interest
9. _____	A savings account that requires a large minimum deposit
10. _____	The purchase of goods or services, without the exchange of money, with a promise of future payment

12 ▸ Understanding Savings Accounts

Exercise 46

Skill Practice

Suppose you are a banker. A new customer wants to know about the three types of savings accounts. Write the advantages and disadvantages of each. Then answer the question that follows.

1. Regular savings account

Advantages:

_____

Disadvantages:

_____

2. Money market account

Advantages:

_____

Disadvantages:

_____

3. Certificate of deposit (CD)

Advantages:

_____

Disadvantages:

_____

4. What qualifications would you need to apply for a loan from this bank? Why?

_____

_____

_____

_____

12 ▶ Expressing Opinions

Exercise 47

Critical Thinking

Read and answer the questions.

1. Some people say that consumers are better off not using credit cards at all. Do you agree or disagree? Give two reasons for your answer.

   _____

   _____

   _____

2. How much of their income do you think people should save each year and why?

   _____

   _____

   _____

3. Every week, Kurt pays his bills first, and then he spends money on things that he enjoys. If he has anything left, he puts it into a savings account. Every week, Janelle puts just $15 dollars into her savings account. Then she pays her bills. If she has anything left, she spends it on things that she enjoys. Whose plan makes more sense to you, Kurt's or Janelle's? Give two reasons.

   _____

   _____

   _____

4. Larry wants to borrow $10,000 from the bank to help start a small business. The bank wants collateral and will charge him interest. A friend offers to loan Larry $10,000 at little or no interest, and she does not ask for collateral. "Just remember who helped you out when you are a big success," the friend says. Which loan do you think Larry should choose, and why?

   _____

   _____

   _____

12 ▶ Comparing Savings Plans

Compare the savings plans. Then answer the questions below.

	Regular Savings	Student Savings	Christmas Club	Money Market	Investment CD
Recommended if you need	Traditional savings		Year-round savings	Variable rate	Fixed rate
Minimum deposit	$100	$25	None	$2,500	$2,500
Interest rate	Variable rate; may change daily Interest paid quarterly		Interest paid quarterly and at maturity	Interest compounded daily	
Monthly fee	None with minimum balance of $300	None until age 21	None	$5 per month	None
Statement	Monthly statement	Not offered	Not offered	Monthly statement	Year-end statement
Withdrawals allowed	Unlimited		Not allowed	Limited	Only one withdrawal

1. Which savings plan would you choose if you were 17 and not working full-time?

   _____

2. Which savings plans could you choose if you wanted interest compounded daily?

   _____

3. Which savings plan would you choose if you wanted a monthly statement and unlimited withdrawals?

   _____

4. Which savings plan would you choose if you had $2,500 to deposit and wanted a variable rate?

   _____

13 ▶ Spending Money

Use what you have learned about money and bartering to answer the following questions.

1. What are two ways that you earn money and two ways that you spend money?

_____

_____

_____

_____

2. Have you ever used bartering? Describe what product or service you offered and what you received in return. Or, describe a situation in which you might use bartering.

_____

_____

_____

_____

3. How would your life change if bartering suddenly replaced the use of money?

_____

_____

_____

_____

_____

_____

13 ▶ Using Checks

A. Suppose that you need to pay your electric bill of $42.19 (forty-two dollars and nineteen cents) to American Utilities. Fill out the check below for the correct amount.

First International Bank   102

_____ *January 1, 2001* _____

PAY TO THE ORDER OF ___*American Utilities*_____ $ [   ]

_____ DOLLARS

MEMO *electric bill-December* _____   *John Q. Smith* _____

⑈0000 55000⑈ 00⑈ 0000   000 000000 0000 2

B. Use what you have learned about checks to answer the questions.

1. How much of America's money supply is made up of checking accounts?

   _____

2. Why are such checking accounts sometimes called "demand deposit accounts?"

   _____

   _____

3. What advantages and disadvantages do you think paying by check has over paying by cash?

   _____

   _____

4. How is a debit card the same as paying by check?

   _____

   _____

13 ▶ Changing Our Currency   **Exercise 51**

In Chapter 13, you read about the $1 Susan B. Anthony coin and the
$2 bill. People did not like these types of currency. Suppose you were
in charge of the U.S. Treasury. Think about the changes you might
make. Use your ideas to answer the questions.

1. What existing coins and bills might you replace? Why?

_____

_____

2. What new coin, bill, or form of currency would you suggest? Draw
a picture of the new currency in the box below.

_____

3. Explain why your new currency would meet the desirable qualities
for money.

_____

_____

_____

4. Because of advances in technology such as debit cards and
transactions by computer, do you think that currency will become
a thing of the past? Why or why not?

_____

_____

_____

14 ▶ Understanding the Fed

Use what you have learned about the Federal Reserve System to answer the questions. Review pages 182–185 if you need help.

1. What is the Federal Reserve System?

   _____

2. When and why was it founded?

   _____

3. How many districts is it divided into?

   _____

4. Which Federal Reserve District do you live in?

   _____

5. In what city is the Federal Reserve Bank for your district?

   _____

6. What are three things that the Fed does?

   _____

   _____

   _____

7. How does the Fed clear checks?

   _____

8. What is the most important job of the Fed?

   _____

   _____

Name _____ Date _____

14 ▶ Writing a Journal Entry

Suppose you, your family, and your friends lived in the year 1907 and experienced a bank panic. Finish each of the journal entries below.

1. What happens on the day of the bank panic?

Date _____

_____'s Journal _____

_____

_____

_____

_____

_____

_____

_____

_____

2. What is life like the day after the bank panic?

Date _____

_____'s Journal _____

_____

_____

_____

_____

_____

_____

_____

_____

14 ▶ Comparing Banks

In Chapters 12 and 14, you read about comparison shopping. You want to open a checking account. Comparison shop the two banks below. Then answer the questions.

	Bank 1	**Bank 2**
Hours open	Monday–Saturday 9–6	Monday–Friday 10–5 Saturday 9–12
Standard checking	$750 minimum balance	$350 minimum balance
Interest checking	$1,000 minimum balance 3% interest	$1,500 minimum balance 2.5% interest
Free checks	Yes	Yes
Monthly service charge	$9.00	$4.50

1. Which checking account would you choose if you had a job that paid $1,000 per month?

   _____

2. Which bank would you choose if you wanted the lowest monthly service charge?

   _____

3. Which bank offers the highest interest on a checking account?

   _____

4. Which checking account has the lowest minimum balance required?

   _____

5. Which bank is open more hours?

   _____

Name _____   Date _____

Study the graph. Then answer the questions below.

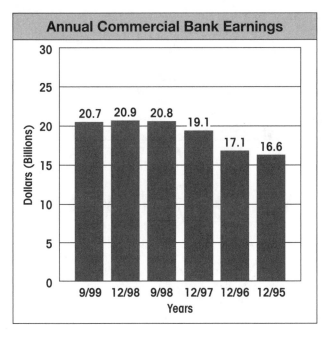

Annual Commercial Bank Earnings

Dollars (Billions)

20.7 20.9 20.8 19.1 17.1 16.6

9/99 12/98 9/98 12/97 12/96 12/95

Years

1. Bank profits rose from $16.6 billion in 1995 to $19.1 billion in 1997. How much more did the banks earn in 1997?

   _____

2. In which year did the banks record the lowest earnings?

   _____

3. In which year did the banks record a $20.9 billion profit?

   _____

4. Banks today often have to pay higher interest rates to attract deposits. Do you think the higher interest rates would reduce or increase the banks' profits?

   _____

5. Do you think banks will lend more money as their profits increase? Why or why not?

   _____

   _____

   _____

15 ▸ Labeling a Graph

Use the terms in the box to label the example of the business cycle.
Then answer the questions below.

Expanding economy	GDP increases	Peak
Contracting economy	GDP decreases	Trough

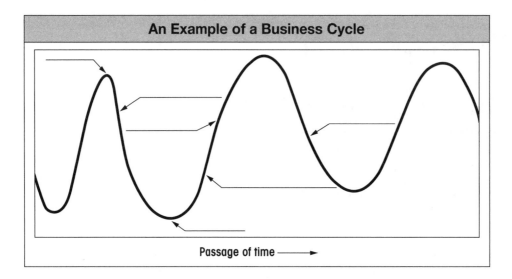

An Example of a Business Cycle

Passage of time ⟶

1. If the GDP decreases, the economy can be in a recession. What
   happens during a recession?

   _____

   _____

   _____

2. During a recession, do you think people should spend more or save
   more? Give two reasons for your opinion.

   _____

   _____

   _____

15 ▶ Finding Out About the GDP

Exercise 57

Critical Thinking

Read the story. Then answer the questions.

An Economic News Conference

President Brown is giving a news conference. She tells reporters that the economy is getting better. "The GDP is higher this year than last year," she says.

"Ms. President," a reporter asks, "is that the real GDP?"

"It sure is!" President Brown replies.

"Ms. President," says another reporter, "it is true that the GDP has been increasing overall. But look at business right now. GDP decreased during the last quarter. We're in a recession."

"Now, wait a moment," the President replies. "We're not in a recession yet. You reporters are quick to think the worst! Next thing you know, you'll be telling me our country is in a depression."

"Okay," says the reporter, "we're not in a recession or a depression, but everybody knows that this contraction of the business cycle will last a long time. Isn't that right?"

"It's hard to predict how long a business cycle will last. But I feel sure that our economy is expanding. Already, I see several signs of that."

---

1. Why did one reporter ask if the President was talking about the "real GDP"?

   _____

   _____

2. The President denied that the country is in a recession. Is she right? Why or why not?

   _____

   _____

3. The President says she sees signs that the economy is expanding. What might some of these signs be?

   _____

   _____

   _____

   _____

15 ▶ Thinking About the GDP

Exercise 58

Critical Thinking

You probably do not wake up wondering what is happening with the GDP. Yet it affects you as it goes up or down. Keep in mind your own part in the economy as you answer the questions.

1. Think about how one article of your clothing is produced. What does the price of the final good include?

   _____

   _____

   _____

2. Without knowing the GDP, how do you think the U.S. economy is doing right now? What makes you think so?

   _____

   _____

   _____

3. You read that an increase in the GDP does not necessarily mean that the country is in good shape. What goods or services do you wish the country were spending less money on? What goods or services do you wish the country were spending more money on? Give reasons for your answers.

   _____

   _____

   _____

   _____

   _____

   _____

15 ▶ Writing Headlines

Exercise 59

Review

Write a newspaper headline for each part of a business cycle listed below. For example, "New Business Owners Say Future Looks Good" is one headline you might see during the expansion period of a business cycle.

1. A period of expansion or growth in the economy

_____

_____

2. At the peak period of a business cycle

_____

_____

3. The GDP decreases for one quarter

_____

_____

4. During a severe recession

_____

_____

5. At the trough period of a business cycle

_____

_____

Name _____   Date _____

Study the graphs below. Then answer the questions.

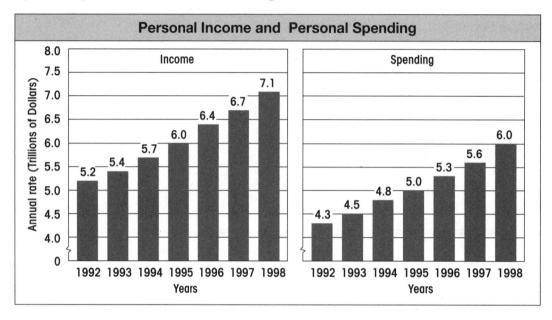

1. Do these graphs indicate an economic expansion or contraction?

   _____

   _____

2. In which year was personal spending at its lowest point?

   _____

   _____

3. In which year did personal income first rise above $6.1 trillion?

   _____

   _____

4. What was the difference (in trillions of dollars) between personal
   income and personal spending in 1995?

   _____

   _____

5. What numbers would you expect the graphs to indicate for 1999?

   _____

   _____

Name _____ Date _____

16 ▶ Studying Inflation

Exercise 61

Review

Write the descriptions and give an example for each of the words below. Review Chapter 16 if you need help.

Words to Know	Description	Example
1. Inflation	An increase in the average price of goods and services	A house that cost $30,000 in 1960 may cost $350,000 today.
2. Deflation		
3. Fixed income		
4. Cost-of-living raise		
5. Demand-pull inflation		
6. Cost-push inflation		

16 ▶ Thinking About Inflation

Exercise 62

A. Describe what kind of inflation would result from the following actions.

1. The cost of lumber doubles

_____

2. Several buyers bid for a famous painting

_____

3. Forest University becomes the best place to get a degree

_____

4. Utility companies raise electric fees

_____

B. Describe how each of the following might respond to a big increase in the cost of grocery items.

1. Someone who has just received a cost-of-living raise

_____

_____

2. A senior citizen who lives on a fixed income

_____

_____

3. A restaurant owner

_____

_____

4. A busy, single parent who is used to buying convenience foods and eating out

_____

_____

16 ▶ Learning About Cost of Living

Exercise 63

Critical Thinking

Use what you have learned in Chapter 16 to answer the questions.

1. Grandpa is reading the car ads in the newspaper. He is upset that cars cost so much today. He tells his granddaughter that his father bought his first car for $375. His granddaughter is very surprised by the low price. Are you surprised, too? Why or why not?

   _____

   _____

   _____

2. The boss tells George that he is her best employee by far. Now George is looking forward to a raise. Do you think he will be happy with a cost-of-living raise? Why or why not?

   _____

   _____

   _____

3. Who do you think worries most about inflation? Why?

   _____

   _____

   _____

4. Goods and services that cost $100 in 1967 cost $391.40 in 1990. If this trend continues, what do you think the Consumer Price Index will show in the year 2020?

   _____

   _____

   _____

16 ▶ Beating Inflation

Exercise 64

Critical Thinking

**Be an inflation beater! List two ways to enjoy each of the following
items at little or no cost.**

1. Books

_____

_____

2. A good meal

_____

_____

3. A movie

_____

_____

4. A new suit

_____

_____

5. A birthday gift for a friend

_____

_____

6. A haircut

_____

_____

7. A vacation

_____

_____

Name _____ Date _____

 17 ▷ **Studying Unemployment**   **Exercise 65**

A. Fill in the chart below. Review Chapter 17 if you need help.

Unemployment

1. Who it includes:

_____

2. How it is measured:

_____

3. Who it does not include:

_____

4. Who it affects the most:

_____

5. How government helps the unemployed:

_____

B. Read and answer the questions.

1. Why is some amount of unemployment seen as normal,
even good?

_____

_____

2. Is the unemployment rate the same across the United States?
Explain your answer.

_____

_____

_____

_____

17 ▶ Identifying Types of Employment

Exercise 66

A. Read each quote. Choose the term from the box that applies. Write the term on the line below each quote.

cyclical unemployment	seasonal unemployment
structural unemployment	frictional unemployment

1. "With my language skills and my background in accounting, I knew that I could do better than this. So I quit my job at the market, moved to the city, and started interviewing at all the big firms."

   _____

2. "Being an assistant ski instructor pays well. But then the snow melts, and the tourists go home. Maybe I can get a job at one of those outdoor cafes. That would get me through the summer, anyway."

   _____

3. "This recession cost me my job. With prices going up, shoppers were watching every penny. The department store just didn't need as many salespeople."

   _____

4. "I had a good job as a secretary until the company changed computer programs. I thought I could get by with my old skills. I was wrong."

   _____

B. Write one example of each type of unemployment listed in the box above.

1. _____

2. _____

3. _____

4. _____

Name _____ Date _____

Giving Advice

Exercise 67

Critical Thinking

Read the situations below. What advice would you give to each of the following people?

1. A high school student who gets turned down for a job as a newspaper reporter

   _____

   _____

   _____

2. An unemployed tour guide with a good driving record

   _____

   _____

   _____

3. A qualified job applicant who feels that she was passed over because of her race

   _____

   _____

   _____

4. A 45-year-old unemployed autoworker who does all his own home repairs

   _____

   _____

   _____

5. A cashier in a small shop who wants to manage a sales team

   _____

   _____

   _____

Name _____   Date _____

Use the tables to answer the questions below.

U.S. Unemployment					
Who Was Out of Work			**States**		
	1999 Rates	**Change Since 1998**		**Feb. 2000 Rates**	**Change Since Jan. 2000**
Nation	4.3%	−0.1	California	4.6%	−0.2
Men	3.5	−0.1	New York	4.7	−0.2
Women	3.9	−0.1	Massachusetts	3.1	+0.1
Whites	3.8	0.0	Florida	3.7	0.0
Blacks	7.5	−0.8	Texas	4.4	+0.1
Hispanics	6.8	−0.6	Pennsylvania	4.1	+0.1
Teenagers	13.4	−1.5	New Jersey	4.1	+0.2
			Michigan	2.7	−0.5
			Ohio	4.3	+0.3
			Illinois	4.3	+0.3
			North Carolina	3.4	+0.2

1. What was the overall unemployment rate in 1999? Had this percentage increased or decreased since 1998?

   _____

2. Which labor-force group had the highest unemployment?

   _____

3. Which labor-force group had the largest decrease in unemployment?

   _____

4. Which state had the highest unemployment rate?

   _____

5. Which two states showed the largest increase in unemployment?

   _____

6. How many states were above the national average in unemployment?

   _____

Name _____   Date _____

17 ▶ Creating a Fact Sheet

Create a fact sheet about unemployment in your area. To get the facts you
need, call or visit an expert in your area. Just look up "Employment" in the
Community Services section of your telephone book.

Unemployment Fact Sheet

1. What is the unemployment rate in your state or area?

_____

2. What employment training services are available?

_____

_____

_____

3. Where does a person apply for unemployment benefits?

_____

_____

_____

4. What is the range in benefits per month?

_____

_____

5. What are the best job opportunities at this time?

_____

_____

_____

_____

---

18 ▶ Helping the Poor

Exercise 70

Skill Practice

A. Complete the chart below. List two examples for each part of the chart.

Transfer of Income to the Poor		
Private Charities	**Social Insurance Programs**	**Social Welfare Programs**

B. Read and answer the questions.

1. Describe one of the social welfare programs that you listed above. What are some ways in which it differs from a private charity?

_____

_____

_____

_____

_____

_____

2. What group of people are most likely to need help from one of the programs above? Why do you think this is so?

_____

_____

_____

_____

_____

18 ▶ Starting a Charity

In Chapter 18, you read about charities—nonprofit organizations that accept donations such as money, goods, and volunteer time and provide aid to needy people. Suppose you could start your own charity. Describe it by answering the questions.

1. What group of people would your charity help and why? What kind of needs might that group have?

_____

_____

_____

2. What name would you give to your charity?

_____

_____

3. There are many different charities in the United States. What are two ways you might let people know about your charity?

_____

_____

4. Give two examples of what people could give to your charity and how it would help.

_____

_____

5. Often, a charity has a famous spokesperson. The spokesperson uses his or her many public appearances to tell people about that charity. For example, the movie star Elizabeth Taylor has helped many AIDS charities. If you could choose anyone in the world to be the spokesperson for your charity, who would it be and why? It could be someone you know or someone famous.

_____

_____

Thinking About Poverty

Use the table below to answer the questions.

Poverty Lines in the United States			
Family Size	**1996**	**1997**	**1998**
1	$7,995	$8,183	$8,316
2	$10,233	$10,473	$10,634
4	$16,036	$16,400	$16,660
6	$21,389	$21,886	$22,228

1. What is a poverty line?

_____

2. In 1998, Marta, who is single, has a monthly income of $575. Is she living above

or below the poverty line? _____ Make a budget for Marta. Will

she be able to save anything? _____ What does Marta's budget

tell you about her standard of living? _____

_____

Marta's Monthly Budget	
Rent	
Utilities	
Food	
Transportation	
Clothing	
Other	

3. Vicki is a single mother raising a child. In 1998, she made $8,500 a year. Was this

above or below the poverty line? _____

18 ▶ Studying Incomes

The Franklin and Carter families each have an annual income of $18,000. The Carter family is living well. It even manages to put some money into savings. The Franklins can barely get by. Use this information to answer the questions.

1. What three factors, besides income, might be affecting each family?

The Carters:

_____

_____

_____

The Franklins:

_____

_____

_____

2. What could the Franklin family do to improve its situation?

_____

_____

_____

_____

_____

_____

_____

_____

_____

19 ▶ Identifying Types of Taxes   Exercise 74

Review

Read each quote. Choose the type of tax from the box that applies.
Then write it on the line below the quote.

estate tax	personal income tax	excise tax	inheritance tax
sales tax	property tax	corporate income tax	social-insurance tax (FICA)

1. "I pay it, my staff pays it, and it all goes to the federal government. Of course, when we retire, we'll get some of it back."

   _____

2. "The way I see it, it's one more good reason not to smoke. Now, if only I could give up driving a car!"

   _____

3. "My grandmother left me some property when she died. That does not mean it was free, however."

   _____

4. "The sweater costs $49.95, but you'll need to add a few dollars onto that."

   _____

5. "I guess I can't complain. I mean, my job does pay a good salary."

   _____

6. "My house is worth more today than when I bought it 10 years ago."

   _____

7. "The company had a big profit this year."

   _____

8. "When she died, she owned several hundred acres of farmland."

   _____

Name _____ Date _____

A. Think about government services and organizations that you and others use
during the year. Add three examples to those shown below. If you need help with
their exact names, refer to the government listings in your phone book.

1. *Setting health and safety standards for foods and drugs–The Food and Drug Administration*

2. *Taking care of state parks and beaches–Parks and Recreation Department*

3. *Getting a driver's license–Motor Vehicle Department*

4. _____

5. _____

6. _____

B. Use the examples listed above to answer the questions.

1. How would life change if these services did not exist at all? Give two examples.

   _____

   _____

2. How would these services be different if private business, not the government,
   provided them? Give two examples.

   _____

   _____

   _____

   _____

3. Which of the above services is most important to you? Do you think that
   more tax money should be spent on that service? Why or why not?

   _____

   _____

   _____

19 ▶ Paying Taxes

Read the story. Then answer the questions.

Tax Time

"So, what's Bert grumbling about today?" joked Alysha, his accountant. She walked through the store to her desk in the back.

"Taxes," said Vera, Bert's wife.

"I am not grumbling," said Bert, "just making a point. How are we going to make a profit with all these taxes we have to pay? We're talking income tax, excise tax, FICA, sales tax—"

"Now, Bert," said Vera, "our customers pay the sales tax—"

"And I, your humble employee, pay FICA just like you," added Alysha.

"Yeah, but what about all the taxes I pay that go for services we never use?"

"Name one," said Vera.

"Public schools," said Bert. "Do we have kids? No. But still we pay. What do we get out of it?"

"What you get," said Alysha with a grin, "is an employee with strong math skills and a degree—just like you asked for in your ad."

Bert laughed. "Okay, okay!"

"And what about all the help we got from the Small Business Administration?" his wife said.

"Hey, you win! I give up! Just call me the Jolly Taxpayer!"

---

1. Bert talked about several kinds of tax. What is one type of tax that he did not mention?

   _____

2. Bert also mentioned excise tax. Do you think that this type of tax is fair? Why or why not?

   _____

   _____

3. Bert and Vera's store is located downtown in a growing city. What kinds of services might their local taxes pay for? Tell how one of these services might benefit the store owners. Explain your answer on a separate sheet of paper.

4. Some economists believe that a true free market economy should have a policy of laissez faire. Do you think Bert would agree? Why or why not? Explain your answer on a separate sheet of paper.

20 ▶ Learning About the National Debt

Read the story. Then answer the questions.

5.6 Trillion Dollars

Tracy and Carla share a newspaper on the bus as they ride to work. Tracy hands the front section of the paper over to Carla. "Why should I care about the national debt?" says Tracy.

"Because it's almost $5.6 trillion," says Carla.

"Oh my, that's a lot of zeroes, isn't it? Still, this country has a lot of taxpayers. What if we all just, you know, pay it off?"

"Do you have $21,000 on you?" laughs Carla.

"Not at the moment," says Tracy. "Okay, so we don't pay it off for a while. So what? I'm sure the government will collect enough money someday."

"It's not that simple," says Carla. "For example, what happens if you don't pay off your credit cards on time?"

"I always pay my credit cards on time. If I didn't, I'd owe the bank even more money, and . . . oh, I see what you mean."

"Exactly," says Carla. "We have to do something about the national debt right now."

"Well, even so, it's not like the U.S. government will ever go bankrupt."

---

1. Carla compares the public debt to a credit card debt. What is she trying to show by making that comparison?

_____

_____

2. To pay off the national debt, who would need to pay $21,000?

_____

_____

3. Tracy says that the government will never go bankrupt. What does she mean?

_____

_____

4. What might happen if a large amount of interest on the national debt were paid to foreign investors?

_____

_____

Name _____ Date _____

 20 ▶ **Understanding the Economy**

The national debt affects everyone in the United States. Share your views about this and other economic issues as you answer the questions. Use a separate sheet of paper if you need it.

1. Some people say that the national debt is the most important economic issue. Others say that unemployment is our biggest worry. Still others point to poverty. What do you think is the most important economic issue? Why?

   _____

   _____

2. In your opinion, which would be more helpful in paying off the national debt:
   (a) raising taxes or *(b)* cutting spending on government programs? If *a*, what type of taxes should be raised and why? If *b*, what programs should be cut and why?

   _____

   _____

   _____

   _____

3. In 1998, the federal government had a budget surplus for the first time since 1960. For the next several years, the government continued to have a surplus. Do you think that it will continue to happen? Why or why not?

   _____

   _____

4. How do you feel about the role of government in the economy? Think about the way the government collects and uses taxes.

   _____

   _____

   _____

   _____

20 ▸ Informing the Public

You are President of the United States in 1960, 1989, and 2020. Each year, you give a speech to the American people about the state of the economy. In your speech, you tell what the economy is like and how you think it will be in the future. You talk about taxes and the government programs that you plan to start, cut, or keep going. Write a speech for each of the years listed below. (If you need more information about the years 1960 and 1989, review pages 258–260 in your textbook.)

1. What speech might you have given in 1960?

_____

_____

_____

_____

_____

_____

2. What speech might you have given in 1989?

_____

_____

_____

_____

_____

_____

3. What speech would you give in the year 2020? Write it on a separate piece of paper and present it to the class.

Name _____   Date _____

Read the following situations. Then write an explanation for each.

1. Kelvin and Diane Jordan see the headline in the newspaper:
   "Federal Reserve Raises Reserve Requirement to Record High." "Oh,
   great," sighs Diane, "I was worried enough about our chances of
   buying a new car." "This sure doesn't help," agrees Kelvin. "It looks
   like we'll be driving that old clunker until the reserve requirement
   goes back down." What does Kelvin mean?

   _____

   _____

   _____

   _____

2. Ms. Ursino calls a meeting of her real estate agents. "Well, folks,
   it looks as if business is going to get better around here. You'll see.
   People were 'just looking' before. But from here on, we may
   actually sell some houses." "That is good news," says one of the
   real estate agents. "But how can you be so sure?" Ms. Ursino replies,
   "Because the Federal Reserve has lowered the discount rate."
   How might lower discount rates affect people who were thinking
   of buying houses?

   _____

   _____

   _____

3. Gus hears a radio ad for his local bank. The ad claims, "Our loans
   are the best in town. You can bank on it." Cute ad, Gus thinks, but
   it's the prime rate that really matters. Why?

   _____

   _____

   _____

Name _____ Date _____

 21 ▶ Studying Fiscal Policy **Exercise 81**

**Answer the following questions. Review Chapter 21 in your textbook
if you need help.**

1. What is fiscal policy?

_____

_____

_____

_____

2. Using fiscal policy, what might the government do when there is
high unemployment?

_____

_____

3. Using fiscal policy, what might the government do when there is
high inflation?

_____

_____

4. Which U.S. Presidents favored a strong fiscal policy?

_____

_____

5. What have critics of fiscal policy said about it?

_____

_____

_____

_____

21 ▶ Studying Monetary Policy   Exercise 82

Answer the following questions. Review Chapter 21 in your textbook if you need help.

1. What is monetary policy?

    _____

    _____

    _____

    _____

2. What might the Federal Reserve do with the money supply when there is high unemployment? Why?

    _____

    _____

3. What might the Federal Reserve do with the money supply when there is high inflation? Why?

    _____

    _____

4. Why does the Federal Reserve encourage or discourage bank loans?

    _____

    _____

5. What are the three ways in which the Federal Reserve encourages or discourages bank loans? List and describe each one.

    _____

    _____

    _____

    _____

    _____

21 ▸ Expressing Opinions   **Exercise 83**

Study the pie chart that shows a "typical" year's spending by the U.S. government. Then answer the questions.

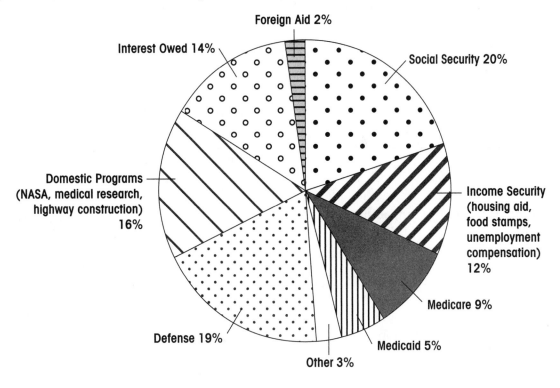

1. Does the government spend more or less money on defense than on Medicare and Medicaid combined? What is the difference (in percent)? How do you feel about this?

   _____

   _____

2. Do you think more money should be spent on domestic programs? Why or why not?

   _____

   _____

3. Suppose you have always held a steady job. Do you think your taxes should be spent on the unemployed? Why or why not?

   _____

   _____

   _____

22 ▷ Understanding Trade

Read and answer the questions.

1. What are two benefits of international trade?

_____

_____

2. What problems can arise because of international trade?

_____

_____

3. What is meant by comparative advantage? Give an example.

_____

_____

4. Waterford crystal glasses are made only in Ireland. Name two other examples of specialization.

_____

_____

5. What is the difference between an import quota and an embargo?

_____

_____

6. What is the difference between free trade and protectionism?

_____

_____

22 ▶ **Understanding Imports**   **Exercise 85**

A. Check some of the food, clothing, high-tech items, and other products in your home, local stores, or at your school. List five items, and tell where they were made. Do you find more imports or items produced in the United States?

Product	Country of Origin	Import or USA Produced?
1.		
2.		
3.		
4.		
5.		

B. Write a detailed paragraph describing what would happen if you could only buy products made in the United States.

_____

_____

_____

_____

_____

_____

_____

_____

22 ▶ Comparing Foreign Currencies   **Exercise 86**

Skill Practice

Study the following foreign currency table. Then answer the questions.

Country	Currency	$1 U.S. Equals	Foreign Currency in $ U.S.
Australia	Dollar	1.64	.61
France	Franc	6.7	.15
India	Rupee	43.57	.0229
Japan	Yen	105.53	.0095
Poland	Zloty	4.07	.2454
Spain	Peseta	171.41	.0058

1. Which country's currency is worth the most?

_____

2. Which country's currency is worth the least?

_____

3. How many zlotys would you get for one U.S. dollar?

_____

4. Suppose a French traveler brought 200 francs into the United
States. If she exchanged them for dollars, how many dollars would
she have?

_____

5. Suppose you were visiting Japan with 1,000 U.S. dollars. If you
exchange them for yen, how many yen would you receive?

_____

Name _____   Date _____

22 ▶ Forming Opinions

Exercise 87

Critical Thinking

The following quotes are opinions, not facts. Below each opinion, write whether you agree or disagree. Then give your reasons.

1. "People would be better off if they only bought goods made in their own countries."

   _____

   _____

   _____

2. "Embargoes affect the country that places them more than they affect the country they are placed against."

   _____

   _____

   _____

3. "Free trade between the United States and Mexico will create more jobs in both countries."

   _____

   _____

   _____

4. "It is important to protect U.S. businesses and workers from foreign competition, even if that means that American consumers have to pay high prices for clothing, cars, and other American-made products."

   _____

   _____

   _____

5. "There should be few or no restrictions on international trade."

   _____

   _____

   _____

23 ▶ Comparing and Contrasting

Read and answer the questions.

1. What are three developed countries?

   _____

   _____

   _____

2. What are three developing countries?

   _____

   _____

   _____

3. In Chapter 23, you read that only 2 percent of the U.S. labor force
   works in farming. Yet U.S. farmers produce most of the country's
   food and enough to export, too. In Chile, about 20 percent of the
   labor force works in farming. Yet most farmers in Chile only grow
   enough for their own families. How would you explain such a
   big difference?

   _____

   _____

   _____

   _____

4. What are two reasons why a country might have a high infant
   mortality rate?

   _____

   _____

5. What are two reasons why a country might have a high
   literacy rate?

   _____

   _____

Name _____ Date _____

 23 Comparing and Contrasting GDP

You have learned that the gross domestic product (GDP) is the value of all goods and services produced by Americans and foreign companies within U.S. borders each year. Compare the per capita GDP of the 10 nations in the chart. Then answer the questions.

1996 Per Capita GDP (approx)			
Canada	$22,000	Peru	$898
Costa Rica	$1,810	Portugal	$13,000
Ireland	$19,000	Switzerland	$25,000
Italy	$20,000	Uganda	$290
Mexico	$8,000	United States	$28,000

1. Which country has the lowest per capita GDP?

   _____

2. Is the per capita GDP of Switzerland more or less than that of Canada? By how much?

   _____

3. Is the per capita GDP of Mexico more or less than that of Costa Rica? By how much?

   _____

4. Choose one of the countries above. Describe its main exports and the kinds of work the people do. Use an encyclopedia, an almanac, or online references.

   _____

   _____

   _____

   _____

Name _____   Date _____

23 ▶ Finding Solutions

Exercise 90

Critical Thinking

You are a newly elected leader of a developing country. The land is
beautiful. You are proud of your history and culture. Now, you want
to improve the standard of living. First, look at possible problems.
Then think about their solutions.

1. You see that the farmers in your country are working much too
hard to produce so little food. List two reasons why this might be
the case.

_____

_____

2. List two changes that would help farmers produce more food with
less labor.

_____

_____

3. Life is harsh for thousands of children in your country. What are
three problems and their causes?

_____

_____

_____

4. List three things that would improve children's lives.

_____

_____

_____

5. What is one way that organizations outside your country might
give help?

_____

_____

_____

Name _____   Date _____

Answer each question with your opinion.

1. Do you think that developed countries have a moral responsibility to help developing countries? Why or why not?

   _____

   _____

2. Which would you rather see more of: foreign aid or foreign investment? Give two reasons for your answer.

   _____

   _____

   _____

   _____

3. Suppose you could spend a year with a volunteer organization such as the Peace Corps. Where would you most want to go, and why? In what ways do you think you could be of help?

   _____

   _____

   _____

   _____

4. Do you think that life in a developed country is *always* better than life in a developing country? Why or why not?

   _____

   _____

   _____

   _____

Name _____   Date _____

23 ▶ Comparing Countries

Follow the instructions below. Review Chapter 23. Use an
encyclopedia, an almanac, or online references to find examples
of life in both developed and developing countries.

1. Suppose you live in Japan, Sweden, or Australia. Write about where
   and how you and your family live. Include details to show that
   you live in a developed country.

   _____

   _____

   _____

   _____

   _____

   _____

   _____

   _____

2. Suppose you live in Haiti, India, or Uganda. Write about where and
   how you and your family live. Include details to show that you live
   in a developing country.

   _____

   _____

   _____

   _____

   _____

   _____

   _____

   _____